HOW TO FADE LIKE GRIFFIN

Barbercation for Today's Barber

HOW TO FADE LIKE GRIFFIN

Barbercation for Today's Barber

By Kendrick D. Henderson

ISBN: 978-0-9980148-6-9
Library of Congress Control Number: 2017951506

Designed and Published by:

The Solid Foundation Group, LLC
PO Box 1483
Smyrna, GA 30081
www.TheSolidFoundationGroup.com

Printed in the United States of America

ACKNOWLEDGEMENTS

First, I'd like to give honors to the Almighty for making me a Master Barber/Master Barber Educator.

Secondly, I'd like to acknowledge my co- contributors for this body of work (Master Barber Brian Henderson, Future Master Barber @RaDuHairTrapHAUS, and published author, Oasis Jones).

In addition, I must acknowledge all of my educators (to-date): Mr. Michael Cheeks, Mr. Corey Thomas, Sgt. Mack, Razor Edge Barbershop, Gate City Barbershop, Heads Up Barber and Beauty, Nu-Image Hair Care Plus, Park West Barber School, Central Carolina Community College, Mr. William Graham, Mrs. Pamela Johnson, Mr. Ed Hooker, No Grease Barbershop, Kool Kuts Barbershop, Richie's Barbershop, He Got Up Barbers in Central Florida, Barber Kings, 71 Barber Institute, Clint's Barbershop, Furious Styles Barbershop, Mr. Fred Walker, The Goat Barbershop, Mrs. Greene, Bull City Barber College, Mr. Jerome Heath, Ms. Tasha and 24/7 Barbershop, A&T Aggies; all barber students that have or will be under my tutelage; and my models, Jamal Dean and Kamari Martin.

I'd also like to acknowledge all barbers that have come before me and that will come after me that honor and practice our glorious profession in a positive light, as well as The Solid Foundation Group for believing in my vision for this project and seeing it to fruition.

DEDICATIONS

I dedicate this body of work to my lost but not forgotten son, Aman Iceen Henderson, and his lil brother that made it, Ahmad Jakari Henderson; to my unborn child with my future wife, Desiree Crump-Henderson...to you both, this book is dedicated; to my backbone and strength, my beautiful mother, Ms. Pamela Gale Henderson; my twin sister, Kyndra Grannie Boyette and her late great husband, Mr. Alan Boyette, and all their children; my elder sister Charmaine Lassiter, her wonderful husband, Derrick Lassiter, and all their children; my two fathers, Author Henderson and Gabe Withfield.

I also dedicate this body of work to every incarcerated soul on this planet – past, present, and future, for we have been chosen to bring change unto this world; and, to my great brother, Richard Riddick, for trusting and believing in me, after all we've been through. We are still a-alikes.

You are all appreciated.

TABLE OF CONTENTS

MATHEMATICAL BARBERING

Introduction: What Are The Supreme Mathematics?

SUPREME IS A WORD MEANING DOMINATE AND MATHEMATICS IS SUPREME TO ALL THINGS IN THIS MATERIAL WORLD. FOR ALL THINGS REVOLVE AROUND MATH, THEREFORE ALL THINGS ARE MATH.

ONCE ONE UNDERSTANDS AND LIVES SUPREME MATHEMATICS THEY BECOME ONE WITH THAT UNIVERSAL FLOW. THIS IS ONE ASPECT OF BEING IN TRUE HARMONY.

SUPREME MATHEMATICS ARE PRINCIPLES THAT REPRESENT THE NUMBER SYSTEM ONE THROUGH NINE (1-9).

1: Knowledge: To look, listen, learn, and most importantly to respect.

2: Wisdom: Ones wise words, ways, and actions

3: Understanding: To cee (see) things for what they truly are and not what they appear to be.

4: Culture-Freedom: Ones divine way of life (principals, morals, and values). To free one's dome (mind) from all negativity.

5: Power-Refinement: Dealing in Truth and preserving ones Integrity. To cleanse one's self from all impurities and negativity.

6: Equality: To deal equal with and in all things, the true science of Oneness.

7: God: Universal Supreme Force and exalted motivating energy of all life.

8: Build or Destroy: To add on to one's life positively and destroy means to eradicate all negativity from one's life.

9: Born: To bring things into existence.

10: Cipher: The completion - 360 degrees of mathematical perfection.

Chapter One
1 = KNOWLEDGE

KNOWLEDGE: TO LOOK, LISTEN, LEARN, OBSERVE, AND MOST IMPORTANTLY TO RESPECT. KNOWLEDGE IS THE FOUNDATION OF ALL THINGS IN EXISTENCE. KNOWLEDGE IS TO KNOW-THE-LEDGE!

This universal mathematical principle allowed me to grow as a barber in many ways. The knowledge of a barber is a combination of one's belief and values, yet most importantly it is the lessons we learn from the theoretical side of our profession.

For all barbers (male or female) this journey starts for us all with Barber School. It is in these times that we are to develop our barber minds and prepare a functioning skill set to advance to the work force.

Going to Barber School was a great time for me! I enjoyed the process that I was engaged in mainly because I went in with a game plan. Being that I was a part of the North Carolina Barber Program we had to do 2 years in Barber School. One year was done on the school side and the second year was our apprenticeship program.

My main goal the first year in Barber School was to consume as much knowledge about our profession and the teachings associated. Not having any prior barbering experience other than getting a haircut, I knew I wouldn't be as good initially as my other classmates. However, this train of thought fueled me to say to myself, "they will not know more than me!"

Knowledge or should I say practicing *the* knowledge has allowed me to grow and develop as a barber and person rapidly. The above characteristics of knowledge holds true in every aspect of barbering.

To look meant that I had to keep my eyes open to everything I was being introduced to. It meant that I couldn't take my eyes off the goal and the agenda at hand. I had to be aware at all times while going through this process given by the Almighty.

To listen meant I had to pay extra close attention to my instructor and listen to him with my mind and not just my ears. A good listener is a good learner, and the best teacher is the most humble student! I also listened to my fellow classmates. We all helped each other along the way throughout Barber School and that was essential to our development. Our ability to communicate and listen to one another made things easier for our instructor.

To learn meant to me that I had to remain teachable! I recall my instructor saying to me that I would be his best student because I started without any initial knowledge nor desire to be a barber. Other classmates had some form of prior experience before going to Barber School and this was great in my eyes.

My instructor knew that I was green as a spring leaf on the tree and this is why he decided to teach me barbering in such a profound manner.

To observe meant I had to go beyond just looking at the people around me work. That alone wasn't going to be enough for me so I chose to observe things much closer. To observe is to do a deeper analysis of a said person, place, or thing. To look further into or to study a thing beyond its surface appearance. This also meant that I had to pay close attention to all details concerning every aspect of barbering and not just while cutting hair. These principals of knowledge have been my pillars throughout my years as a barber thus far.

The most important aspect to knowledge to me is RESPECT. This is a never-ending subject so I'll be brief! Respect and knowledge are one because all things in existence deserve its God given respect. Respect is the backbone of our profession. There must be a level of respect for the barber and the clients in our profession. Respect must be earned and preserved by all barbers. However, we must respect others first before we can expect to be respected.

In fact, to go deeper, we must begin to respect ourselves as barbers and professionals to earn the respect we want others.

Knowledge is the foundation of all things in existence and knowing this fact I made it the foundation of my barbering career. The more I know as a professional the more opportunity I will have to earn and help others. Knowledge is to learn, so learn every day and advance your barber mind as well as your skill set.

Chapter Two
2 = Wisdom

WISDOM: ARE ONES WISE WORDS, WISE WAYS AND ACTIONS. WISDOM IS THE CORRECT APPLICATION OF KNOWLEDGE.

My second year in Barber School was very challenging mainly because it was more skill-set based and less curriculum based. I had become so comfortable with the classroom and mastering our teachings that by the time I made it to year two I was less motivated. I had a great fear of failure my second year in Barber School. With one year remaining I knew I had to improve my cutting skills before I was to be released. The principles of wisdom helped me greatly to make it through this journey as a barber.

One's wise words are very much needed to achieve success in this business. Knowing how to speak to people and knowing what to speak about is wisdom. Everybody is not attracted to the same subjects and as a barber you must always know who is in your presence, for this is a tangible profession. People are so judgmental nowadays when it comes to barbering because of social media and corporate exploitation. I've always done the knowledge to the likes and dislikes of clients. One of the main complaints our clients make are 'barbers don't listen to them and are rude (vainly selfish).

Failure to listen to your clients is not wisdom for to have wisdom one must first apply knowledge, which is to look, listen, learn, observe, and most importantly to respect.

Obtaining barber wisdom in this profession takes years to acquire. It takes many days and nights of commitment to your craft with the most vital attribute being able to absorb wisdom from their peers that preceded them. Trial and error in this profession has shaped and molded our culture into the very art we practice today as barbers. Our predecessors did the knowledge to their trials and errors and brought forth wisdom that allows us not to make the same mistakes should one apply the accumulated knowledge correctly.

As a professional barber, one's ways and actions must always be accounted for by self, and in direct relation to whom they truly are as a person. Meaning who you are as a person is who you are as a barber! As an instructor for Park West Barber School I use to teach our students, "be who you say you are because you never know who is watching!"

As a professional it is imperative to speak and act in accordance with the utmost professionalism. The principals of wisdom will keep one in tune with the above law for success as a barber. It is highly important to know what type of barber you want to be before entering the work force in today's culture. With so much individualism and industrialization of the business being promoted I've witnessed barbers fall by the way side. When one knows who they are and who they seek to be, then and only then will they achieve barber wisdom.

Chapter Three
3 = Understanding

UNDERSTANDING IS SEEING THINGS FOR WHAT THEY
ARE AND NOT WHAT THEY APPEAR TO BE. UNDERSTANDING IS
ALSO THE MERGING OF KNOWLEDGE AND WISDOM TO BRING
FORTH THAT CRYSTAL CLEAR MENTAL PICTURE.

Man-Oh-Man, understanding is so beautiful! That clear
mental picture of understanding will save the one who applies
their knowledge, time and wisdom correctly.

Of course, in Barber School my level of understanding
was very low, mainly because I had to grow in knowledge and
wisdom. One main area I recall struggling with understanding
was that of the art of fading. It seems like no matter how much I
did the knowledge, no matter how much wisdom I received
from my instructor, or how many times I tried to draw a clear
mental picture I continued to fall short of glory.

It wasn't until I had been cutting repeatedly for my first
3 years as a barber that my understanding began to grow and
shine in regard to fading; however, it was my overall
understanding of barbering that gave me the greatest growth as
a barber.

Receiving wisdom from some very elite barbers over the years help fashion my barber mind and integrity. Most notably is Mr. Harris of Gate City Barbershop. This is my "Barber Father" for he was able to help me unlock that clear mental picture of understanding. I truly began to grow when I started to cee things for what they really were and not how they appeared to be. Also by becoming an instructor and ascending to this next level in my barbercation my understanding as a barber blossomed. Now I was able to not only understand but I was able to share and teach my understanding to others giving light to the dark areas they would have to face. This is the gift of understanding as a barber. Each one must teach one according to their own understanding!

When one learns and respects the teachings they've been taught and lives and presents themselves professionally and honestly, they will develop a keen understanding of themselves, their profession, and all parties associated therein.

Understanding is the best part! Develop your ability to understand things in its natural and original form then you can watch another world of barbering unfold. You will find yourself in pursuit of advancement of the craft more so than the advancement of your bank account. Understanding of this way of life will have you fueled by passion more so than paper. Your clients and co-workers will cee a difference in you when your understanding lights the way for your knowledge and wisdom to shine through.

Chapter Four
4 = Culture/Freedom

CULTURE IS A WAY OF LIFE AND FREEDOM IS THE STATE OF BEING FREE.

The accumulation of knowledge and wisdom brings forth understanding of our glorious culture of barbering. Barbering is a natural way of life and not an Industry in all reality.

A way of life are things that are done naturally. Barbering is a science and an art that has been fashioned and developed over the years. Our history teaches us how our profession has advanced and declined over the years.

One might ask what is the difference between the two, but the answer is clear if you truly understand what you are actually engaged in as a barber. Barbering as a way of life is going to Barber School, graduating and getting your license, and then choosing where you will serve as a barber. In actuality, this is our profession in a nutshell. Yet the industry side for barbers is more complex. Industry barbering is more systematic and controlled which robs the barber of their freedom. Instead of being free, barbers become employees for outside companies and corporations that exploited our culture for the pursuit of mass financial gain. Barbers in turn lose vital aspects of themselves trying to "fit in" an industrialized structure of barbering.

With freedom comes responsibility, true indeed but giving the responsibility to another that which you have the ability to do yourself is not freedom. Do barbers need to be more responsible? Yes! Who doesn't need to be more responsible in business?! Judgment of barbers and our characters have been under attack by those on the outside looking in trying to capitalize off our hard work, blood, sweat and tears.

Our way of life has been tried and tested from the beginning of time until the present, it's up to us to add on to it, not to take away from it. The freedom of this culture comes with understanding that a barber is a server of the people. Without the people how can you be a barber? Our way of life is not to be completed but to be continued with the goal of furthering its goodness and allow our flaws to help fashion the future for barbers to follow.

The culture of barbering is the service to man, woman, and child. The freedom therein is not to be exploited nor misused. Understanding the limits of your freedom along with understanding the difference between way of life and industry will bestow wisdom upon the individual expelling their knowledge of the art beyond expectation.

Chapter Five
5 = Power/Refinement

*POWER IS THE ABILITY TO INFLUENCE OTHERS
POSITIVELY WHILE AFFECTING THEM IN A PRODUCTIVE WAY.
REFINEMENT IS TO CLEANSE ONESELF OF ALL IMPURITIES
SPIRITUALLY, MENTALLY, AND PHYSICALLY.*

The power of our way of life is priceless! Who do you know that is more influential than a barber? Sure. That question has a lot of egoism attached, yet it's still a good question. Our clients see or visit their barber more than their doctor. Our clients visit us more than they go to church! In all reality, a barber is one of the greatest weapons in America's communities. As barbers we have the ability to influence people in a positive way or a negative way. Our clients not only trust what we say they actually act out on the things their barber introduces to them. They cling to our conversation in the barbershops. They look to us to know what is current in the world no matter the industry.

We also possess the power to heal people by way of the sense of touch. Barbers that understand this power usually take their craft a bit more serious than the average barber. Yet it's more barbers in the world that think that our potential to earn money or finances is our power.

Barbers that think that money is our true power are not in tune with our history. If this was our true power what does that say about our forerunners that didn't get paid for their services monetarily? Were they less of a barber than we are because we get money for our services and they didn't? Exactly. In my book, they were better barbers than we are because they held true to the culture. They protected the culture by preserving their teachings and finding ways to advance the culture to make things easier for others to employ.

Refinement of one's self, spiritually, mentally, and physically on a daily basis is vital to your health as a barber. To cleanse one's self is to give one's self a fresh start. We all need fresh starts in our lives. By giving yourself a fresh start on a daily basis your giving yourself a chance to recognize and correct your mistakes as they happen.

When I first apply the gas (wake-up) in the morning the first thing I do is give praise to something higher than myself for my awaking. This act in itself is cleansing me internally of egoism before my feet ever hit the floor. This acknowledgement of a higher power sets the foundation of my focus throughout the rest of my day. Mentally I cleanse for my daily personality by listening to positive music while getting dressed and prepared for work. Physically of course I attend to my personal hygiene, which is highly vital in our profession. Body odor of a barber or a client during a service is direct disrespect to the other party. So as we see, refinement is very key to success as a barber. Cleanliness is next to Godliness!

When we as barbers take time to learn our powers as servers of the people, take the time to obtain correct barber wisdom, and take time to understand our culture then we will know freedom as barbers. Then we will not have a problem being one in unity as barbers giving us greater power as a UNIT instead of self engulfed individuals.

Chapter Six
6 = Equality

EQUALITY IS TO BE EQUAL AND DEAL EQUAL WITH ALL THINGS. EQUALITY MEANS ONE.

My first day of Barber School my instructor told us that barbering was a fraternity or a brotherhood and that we always came to each other's aid when in need. This was the glue that bonded me to this way of life early in my career. I've always been the type of brother that loved oneness amongst others. In my mind, this meant that I had family all around the world!

Equality in our way of life is vital for our growth and production because the more we are as one in our profession the less we are divided as an industry. Competition and exploitation of our way of life has divided us over the years almost to a point of no return. Most barbers now a day will only help another barber or barbers if they themselves can get paid. This is not Equality! This is not correct barber unity!

Equality as barbers means that we must find a way to be one. Yet in all reality we are already one when we truly understand who we are. The term (barber) we use to describe ourselves makes us one. The word barber is not a person itself, yet it's a spirit that has to be discovered, developed and delivered.

19

The term derived from the Latin word "barba" which means 'beard", and any conscious mind know that a beard is not a person. A true barber will know that they must identify with the attributes of the beard that makes up or describes the characteristics of a barber. An individual whom displays wisdom, strength, and beauty is living out the attributes of the beard.

Being one with your profession ensures growth within. As barbers we must learn how to separate money from the equation of our oneness in order to be one. Money and egos are the two biggest cripplers to our unity or oneness in our profession.

Equally share your powers with the world so that they will all know the freedom of our oneness as we seek to refine our lives and the lives of others. Building a way of life for all to benefit from as we understand the relationships we fortify for years to come.

Chapter Seven
7 = God

GOD MEANS THE MOST HIGH OR WISDOM, STRENGTH, AND BEAUTY.

The foundation of every barber is the Most High for this science is God created. I was taught as a child that, "God don't like ugly", so if this were true whom else would create beauty. Man, woman, and child are not the creators of beauty. God created beauty for he himself is beautiful! God gave man the ability to cultivate beauty so that we may know his appearance. God gave us the ability to cultivate beauty so that we may share his beauty with others. All things beautiful are looked at as being the Most High and anything of ugly is that of the devil.

Having a firm foundation in the Most High helps keep us grounded as barbers. There are a lot of temptations in the world today and we all can use something to keep us focused and safe out of harm's way. As barbers we have two major areas that we suffer in, saving money and creating residual income, which builds generational wealth.

By giving ourselves something else to stand on beside ourselves like a belief in the Almighty we align ourselves with a different type of success. A lot of barbers seek to be worldly rich while I have grown to understand that it's about being Heaven rich.

21

When we practice barbering we are actually doing the work of the Most High. When we touch our clients, we are healing them. When we upgrade the standard of our client's appearance we are doing the work of God, the true creator of beauty.

God's oneness cleanses our power to influence the world by way of our culture giving understanding to who we truly are and represent as professional barbers.

Chapter Eight
8 = Build or Destroy

TO BUILD MEANS TO ADD ON TO YOUR LIFE POSITIVELY AND DESTROY MEANS TO ERADICATE ALL NEGATIVITY FROM ONES LIFE.

In this way of life building and destroying are the tools we use to create our careers and lives as professional barbers. We add and take away from our personal lives every day. We also add and take away from the lives of those we come in contact with every day as well.

In reality we either build the lives of others or we can have a helping hand in destroying others. When I gained understanding of this mathematical principle I began to take my role as a professional barber more serious. The ability to add on to someone's life is another skill bestowed upon man as a barber. Clients are like sponges in the barbershop. They soak up everything in this environment and that is why it is important to know if you are adding to their lives as barbers or are you taking away from their lives.

This is where your wisdom as a barber comes into play. There will be some clients that can tolerate any and everything in the barbershop and then there are clients that like certain things in and about the barbershop. In all reality, the barbershop is a direct reflection of its location and housing environment.

Building and destroying is simply one learning from their mistakes or trial and error. Enjoy your growth as a barber. Use your flaws to sharpen your strong points. Keep the things that are good and productive for your life and career and get rid of the things that will hinder your life and career. This is simple mathematics.

At a point in my career somewhere around my 3rd or 4th year as a barber I found myself at a glass ceiling. This glass ceiling was the next level in my career, yet, at first, I viewed it as a setback or a dead end. This train of thought was only my youthful ignorance as a barber being activated, however, experiencing this crossroad in my barber career forced me to look within myself and that's when I began the process of building and destroying.

The first thing I did was add on to my life by going to Wake Tech Community College for a continuing education program to receive my instructor's license. In order to add this new level of barbering to my life and career I first had to eradicate a few things out of my life. I had to make a change or changes in order for things to change for me. This is the power of build and destroy.

Build what is of good and destroy all things of bad in your life and success God will grant. For the oneness of all things is power in our culture when one applies correct understanding to the wisdom and knowledge that has been tried and tested over the years.

Chapter Nine
9 = Born

BORN MEANS TO BRING INTO EXISTENCE! AS A BARBER OUR ABILITY TO MANIFEST THINGS SUCH AS OUR KNOWLEDGE AND OUR SKILL SET UNMATCHED TO ANY OTHER PROFESSION. BARBERS IN ALL REALITY ARE SCIENTIST AND WE STUDY ALL ASPECTS OF LIFE.

When we service our clients, we are borning our talents and the ability to envision the end result before beginning the services. These are a couple of things that we bring into existence every day in the barbershop. We bring forth either good experience for our clients or bad experiences. This means that the power to born must be fully understood by one in order to ensure that you are bringing things that are fruitful into existence.

There are a lot of bad habits that barbers are exposed to everyday in the barbershop. Over the years a lot of things have been taken for granted by barbers and our clients have had to pay the price. We as barbers bring joy or unhappiness to clients our entire careers. We are the main ingredients in a healthy way of life. We strive every day to be better at what we do so that we may born more for our clients and ourselves. Born is our ability to make things "BE" so we as professionals must be conscious of our powers and abilities at all times.

27

Born things that will add to the world and not take away. To be born is to enter a state of reality or existence that elevates and sustains a positive way of life that benefits all.

Chapter Ten
10 = Cipher

CIPHER MEANS COMPLETE.

Understanding the power of the cipher helped me in more ways than one as a barber. Two very important lessons were born to me by way of this mathematical principle. The first lesson I learned was to complete any and all projects before moving to the next project. As a thinking man, I'm always trying to find ways to improve everything I possibly can. Unlike most people the more I have to do the more I usually get done. However, over time I found myself giving away more ideas than I actually acted on or completed. This led me to having more things unfinished than completed which was an error. The minute I slowed down and started putting things in a timeline to be completed I started to grow and develop these projects with ease.

The second lesson I was blessed to learn which deals with the power of this mathematical principle was watch those you keep around you. My ex -wife taught me this very important lesson. She told me that if I wanted to be a business owner then I needed to start hanging out with business owners. She said if I wanted people to listen to me then I had to change the way I spoke to people. It was little things like these words that allowed me to see the fruit therein that I was missing.

29

You are only as strong as the people you keep around you. It's important in your aims of success to keep people around you that will complete you and not take away from you. The cipher has value when knowledge is added to the cipher – tenfold.

Make sure "when you add to your cipher" it increases your value as a person and professional. Anything that is not complete is not whole and anything that is not whole isn't complete. To be complete as a barber one must respect the wise teachings that share understanding of our profession. This gives us power to cleanse everyone or everything we service, for the work of the Almighty we use to build people up and destroy what's not helpful to their growth in order to bring into existence what's always been and always will be, "barbering as a natural way of life!"

P.E.A.C.E.

HISTORY
OF THE FADE

In our glorious profession image and the perception of image is everything! Everyone in the world has different reasons for getting their hair cut. Also, everyone in the world has a different way they like for their hair to be cut. This is the very lifeline of our profession – the people's desire to look a certain way. We, as barbers, acquire the ability to help aid and assist our public with these wishes and desires.

In this particular body of work, we will be discussing one of the most popular looks in our profession, which is the "Fade". First thing one should know is that there are many different variations of this particular haircut. Most times this haircut is known by many different names depending on where you are geographically. No matter the name or style of the fade there is still a basic concept to successfully achieving this haircut. This you will learn in this body of work and then some.

Constant research of this subject has led me to an exciting story of the "Fade".

It's been reported that the "Fade" originated as a military cut back in the 50's, yet it has morphed into a universal signature of style in its own right. The fade has been worn by many in one variation or another. Men and even women at some point in time have experienced this most popular haircut. It takes great skill and patience to master this haircut for it is a precision cut. The fade takes care and a barber must be willing to pay attention to close detail.

"NO TWO BARBERS FADE ALIKE!"

While in Barber School I recall being afraid to cut a fade more than I was of shaving. Honestly, I had excelled with my razor work quicker than I did with my clippers. It took quite some time for me to overcome my fear of cutting a fade in any version. Mainly because I couldn't grasp the concept of fading that was being taught to me at that time. Not to take anything away from my instructor, but, "there is a barber in there, let him out" was not enough for me to grow confident with my ability to perform this cut.

Needless to say, the first time I ever did a fade it came out horrible! Really. All jokes aside. I really bricked on my first fade. Mainly due to fear and the lack of knowledge, what was supposed to be a low taper fade ended up being a low bald fade cut by another student barber. That's right. I had to be bailed out which was allowed by my instructor. Truthfully, I didn't mind because after about the first hour I was lost, drained, and praying I didn't have to fight this brother.

"EITHER YOU'RE GOING TO PAINT OR BE A PAINTER!"

In 2012, I migrated to Greensboro North Carolina to embark on a fresh marriage and continue barbering at Gate City barbershop.

Who could know besides the Almighty that the very haircut I was most afraid of would become my signature cut in a historical barbershop. In retrospect, I can honestly say that 80% of my haircuts while at Gate City were fades.

Under the careful watch of seasoned barbers and most importantly our elder Mr. Harris, I honed my eye for blending and fading at a remarkable speed. Mr. Harris taught me a very valuable lesson in barbering when he said, "when you can make a man look the way he wants to look, but at the same time make him look like he never thought he could look before," then you will always have a job.

He also taught me that anyone can paint, but a painter knows how to make a living off his work (painting). Wisdom like this resonates in my barber soul constantly!

With a steady supply of college clientele from A&T University my name as a barber began to spread. My fading techniques created a look for my clients that was distinguish throughout the city.

Fade Griffin became a household name within a three-year span. Fades became my most sought out haircut and I enjoyed every minute of my growth and development as a barber.

"THE MORE YOU LEARN, THE MORE YOU WILL EARN!"

As an instructor working for Park West Barber School in Greensboro North Carolina as well as managing a newly opened barbershop (Heads Up Barber & Beauty) I was able to enhance my knowledge as a barber which in turn strengthened my skill set. After growing beyond Gate City, I knew I had to keep the spirit of my barber father Mr. Harris alive so that his wisdom would continue to magnify within me.

Humbly I recall being a very different type of instructor than my instructor Mr. Cheek. Mr. Cheek very rarely cut hair while teaching in Barber School. In fact, it was like an act of divine blessing whenever he picked the clippers up. I myself would literally get sick watching our students cut, and all I could do is stand there dressed all nice and watch. Yes, other professionals basked in their position as instructor while I was always ready to get down and dirty. Every day I was cutting someone's hair because the barber inside was dying to express his skills.

Balancing the spirit of an instructor and barber can be challenging and it takes great concentration and patience. It was during these times I successfully honed and refined all my skills as a barber. The things that I over looked as a barber student I made sure I mastered as an instructor. The average barbers only see Barber School one time in their barber career.

The furthering of your education, as a barber is key to truly understanding the heart and soul of our profession.

The more you learn as a barber the more you will earn because you will be able to do more as a professional. Truthfully In 4 years I went from making 40 cents a day to making $40,000 a year, mainly because I furthered my education as a barber which strengthened my skill set. True wealth as a barber is not in your ability to cut hair but in your ability to learn and master the process and the rules and regulations associated with it.

"WHO IS FADE GRIFFIN"?

My love for fading is my personal lifeline as a barber. No other haircut I perform excites me like a fade does!

The name Fade Griffin came to be while I was serving at Gate City. However, the foundation of my barber name started while I was serving my last year in prison at 025 in Wilmington North Carolina.

Around this time I was preparing for my return to the so-called free world, yet I was more than focused as a barber. My cutting was getting stronger with every cut. I recall using my Oyster 76's for every haircut because at this time this was my favorite clipper. Mind you this was before I ever had a chance to cut with a pair of Andis Masters. The 76's are a pair of detachable clippers that use different sized blades for cutting and detailing.

At 025 all I cut was fade after fade because I wanted to be ready for the barbershop. I wanted to have my blend so tight that everybody would want my fades. That was my motivation.

This was in the year 2010-2011 and Blake Griffin was very popular in the NBA. If you recall, this brother was dunking on everybody.

I remember saying in the shop one day at 025 (just horsing around), "my new name is Blade Griffin because 80% of my fades are slam dunks like 80% of Blake Griffin shots are slam dunks."

From this joking around in the barbershop came my identity as a barber, in which three years later, I turned into a barber, company and a brand. At Gate City, the named slightly changed from Blade Griffin to Fade Griffin. As a company, I added the word "BY" to distinguish the name of the company from myself as an individual barber. By Fade Griffin truly represents the people whom continue to help me become the barber I'm continuously becoming. The people make us working barbers in the barbershop, because if no one sits in your chair you don't have a job. Likewise, if you don't further your education as a barber and experience new levels in barbering you will not have a job.

Some of today's barbers think that a barber name for himself or herself is a trend or something that you can just make up instead of earning. Your barber name is your identity and that name is originally the name on your barber's license. This is your barber name, brand, and identity as a barber! Yet there is nothing wrong with nicknames as barbers or creating your own name as a barber as long as you know and understand the ethics of our profession.

"A GOOD NAME IS WORTH MORE THAN GOLD"

In 2015, I learned more about barbering and barbers than I ever had in my entire career, thus far. After teaching for Park West for 2 years I was more than ready to get back in the field. The barbershop was calling my name. I cut in Virginia, Georgia, Florida, Louisiana, and Texas. I obtained my barber's license in Florida and was networking with six different barber boards to increase my knowledge of barbering abroad.

Prior to working at Park West, I never knew that it was legal for a barber to produce his or her own system for haircutting. The Park West fade was a system of fading designed by the owners of PW. Unlike our students my instructor never really showed us how to cut yet he did educate us on the laws associated with haircutting. He allowed us to come into our own as barbers, meaning he allowed us to learn how to cut on our own.

Utilizing the knowledge and wisdom I've gained over years, while serving in Laredo I successfully created a system of fading that I've been using my entire career. During a haircut on a straight hair client I discovered how to not only describe my system but also how to record it and teach others. Simplicity being the key to success I kept in mind that all students learn different so I kept things simple.

It's my only intention to inspire and educate those that strive to grow in this profession. In no way am I saying that my system is the *best* way to fade, nor am I comparing it to another system of fading that may exist. All I'm simply saying is I've study, learned, created, and have put my system to the test numerous times.

BINARY BARBERING

Welcome to Binary Barbering 101

"What is Binary Barbering?" is probably the first question that comes to mind when hearing this terminology.

The answer is simple! Binary Barbering is simply using mathematical principles to define and help memorize certain laws and principles associated with hair cutting.

While incarcerated at 025 I enrolled in a telecommunications class wherein I learned of the science of binary code. My instructor put the understanding of this system of math in a nutshell. He said that binary code was a series of 0's and 1's, which was basically read as "on" or "off" to a system such as a computer. Using this system of fading you will learn the relationship between the on's and off's, and how they correspond with haircutting.

Before attempting to learn this system of fading I highly recommend that you play at least one intense game of chess. If you lack the knowledge to play chess then at least meditate in silence for about 10 minutes to open up your creative mind for learning. In reality, the simplest thing to learn sometimes can be the hardest. Learn by heart and use this system as prescribed and you will grow effortlessly.

Things that will strengthen your fading abilities:

Learn the areas or sections of the head. This is important because the sections of the head serve as the foundation to haircutting. One will learn that hair grows in different directions depending on what section of the head the hair is in.

Knowing the sections of the head will serve as a conscious reminder of the above fact concerning the direction of hair growth.

Sections of the head: Apex (top), crown, parietal ridge, right Temple, left Temple, nape, frontal, right side burn, left side burn, and occipital bone.

Learn the seven facial shapes. This is important because by knowing the facial shapes this will help the barber in the envisioning process yet it will also help the barber to maximize a client's strong points and minimize their weak points. It also serves in helping a client know what cut or style looks right or best on them.

Seven facial shapes: round, square, inverted triangle, pear, diamond, oblong, and oval.

Learn the anatomy of hair and the laws associated with it. This is important because the more you learn and understand about the nature of hair the greater your ability in manipulation of it. There are certain laws associated with hair that we often overlook in Barber School. These laws are the very foundation in delivering a respect worthy haircut for your clients.

Hair structure: cuticle (outer most layer), cortex (heart of the hair shaft), and medulla (inner most layer).

Textures of hair: fine, coarse, and medium.

The size of a person's hair shaft determines the texture of their hair.

Learn correct client control. This is important because like myself most barbers cut at an angle, so correct head positioning of your client during haircutting is key. This is also important for maintaining the integrity of your health as a barber.

- No cell phone use while cutting
- No chin on chest cutting
- Limit client movement
- Gain clients trust in giving you total control over the service
- No slouching in the barber chair...etc.

Use the T-Zone to make reference points for creating front design line and C's of the sideburn area.

Learn the parts of your tools especially your clippers: still blade, cutting blade, heel, adjusting lever, adjusting strew, on/off switch, cord.

Pay close attention to growth change and direction while haircutting

Binary Barbering 101: Bald Fade

Set-up: Tools and materials

- Clean and sanitize station
- Combs
- Brushes
- Andis Masters
- Andis BGRV
- Andis T-Outliners
- Attachment combs (guards)
- Shears
- Neck strips
- Drape
- Mirror
- Disinfectant
- Styling products (gel, oil sheen, temp color, etc.)
- Wahl's shaver
- Changeable razor

Step 1: Client Consultation and Draping

After you conduct a thorough consultation, and hair & scalp analysis with your client, properly drape them for the desired service and proceed.

Learn the art of Envisioning. Envisioning is the most important tool we use as a barber! This is the barber's ability to see and know the end result of a service before they get started. In other words, a barber must be able to look into muddy waters (client consultation) and spot dry land (finished product).

Envisioning is an intrinsic ability that must be honed by the barber. Reputation is the best teacher for the acquiring of this skill set. The greater your ability to envision the more satisfied your clients will be.

NOW LET'S GET READY TO CUT!

Step 2: Establish Overall Length (Mountain Top)

Note: Keep in mind the hair cut that we are using the system on to establish is a Bald Fade with a 1 against the grain.

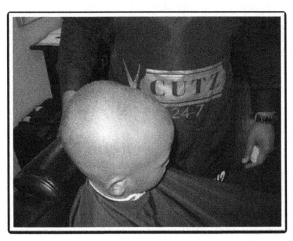

Knowing the sections of the head is the foundation of this system. In binary barbering the head has been divided into 4 sections or panels in which I call "Fading Zones". Remember in Barber School when you first learned how to part your mannequin's hair into 4 sections for a blunt cut? This is the same concept!

Starting at the top of the head at its highest point (Apex) or (Mountain Top) you see the head has been divided into 4 fading zones starting from right temple to left temple. For left-handed barbers, everything is the complete opposite.

These fading zones are labeled North, East, West, and South, spelling the word "NEWS". This is an easy way to remember what section of the head you're cutting in.

When starting our bald fade using this system, the first thing we do is start at the mountaintop and establish the desired length of our client, which is a one against the grain.

Make sure you use smooth and even strokes when cutting the mountain to ensure a clean cut. Once you have established the top portion of the cut proceed to the next step.

Step 3: Establish Framework (frontal line-up)

Traditionally in the barbershop the shape-up or edge-up is performed last in the service.

However, in binary barbering we will address this area sooner. Establishing the design line or the edge-up can make or break your haircut as a barber.

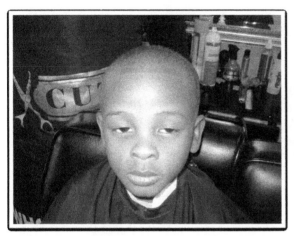

When shaping-up my clients, I envision placing my picture (haircut) in a frame (edge-up) to not only protect what is precious to me, but also to enhance the quality and appearance of my work (picture/haircut).

Think about it! The line-up on a bald fade is just the frontal area and a portion of the side view of a client's profile. Unlike outlining the entire perimeter there is less work to do. By establishing the framework before fading this gives the barber a greater sense of envisioning as you work closer to completion of the haircut.

Step 4: Establish the Equator (first guideline)

The first guideline will be established as a bald fade so we will establish this guideline with our Andis t-outliners.

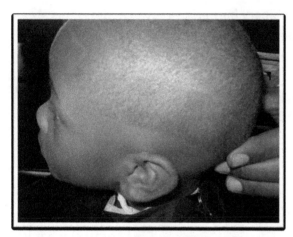

To ensure that we don't make a hard line while placing our guideline we will turn our trimmer belly down and tap and drag downward. It's kind of like beveling in the opposite direction. I refer to the first guideline as the "equator" because the guideline is in the middle of the head just as the equator is to the earth.

Once the equator is established, immediately begin clean work. You can use a razor or electric shaver to do the work (it's up to you).

NOW LET'S BEGIN BINARY BLENDING!!!

Step 5: Establish the Stopping Point

Now that the ground floor of our haircut has been established we can begin the blending process. Using your Andis' Masters we will proceed to step 5, which is to establish the stopping point, which is to fade up to the parietal ridge.

Take a look on the side of your Masters and you'll see 5 notches or grooves for measuring different lengths of hair to be cut.

In binary barbering we always begin blending and fading at the center point of these notches, which is known as ON #1. Once you have your clipper set at ON #1 begin to cut up to about a ½ inch from the parietal ridge, which will appear to create another guideline. This guideline is only the raising of your weight line. Remember fading is like removing the clouds so that the sun can shine. It's hard to blend correctly with weight present. Remove your weight (clouds) before fading so that your blend (sun shine) can come shining through for the world to see and adore.

Step 6: Blend Parietal Ridge

One of the most important keys to blending in the parietal ridge area of the head is to stay off the heal of the clipper and bevel the weight line out to your perfection.

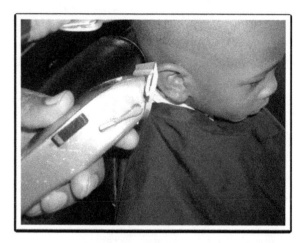

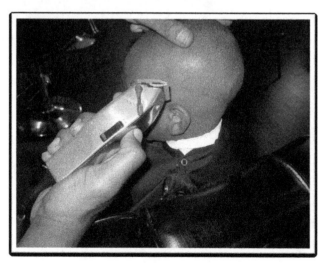

Place your master clipper on ON #2, which should leave your clipper blade all the way open to a 1. Begin to bevel at an angle and the weight line will not only begin to reduce in appearance but it will also begin to blend in with the rest of the haircut. Complete this process until the entire parietal ridge has been blended to match the mountaintop. Also, most times in this area you can cut with the grain at an angle with your masters to reduce bulk before blending depending on the type of fades being performed.

Step 7: Remove the Equator (initial guideline)

In Barber School, I remember a rule of fading our instructor taught us, "whatever you put your line in with, use the same thing to get it out."

Even though this rule held to be true over the years of my infant career I've found other ways to remove my lines of demarcation.

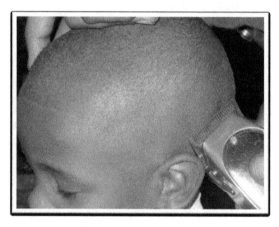

When removing your lines of demarcation be sure to employ the right amount of tension and bevel with precision.

Once the equator has been fully removed from around the head your fade is nearing completion.

Step 8: Polish the Cut

Mr. Harris taught me a very valuable lesson about your ending of a good haircut. I recall him saying, "Not polishing a haircut is like giving your client a steak on a trash can top."

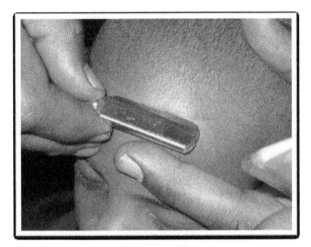

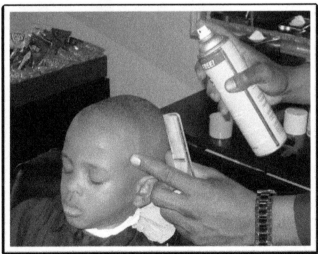

Polishing the haircut is that extra time and care one as a master barber takes to ensure his/her client is fully served. How one works in this area will be based upon the barber. Polishing the cut this is where the razor work is key. The use of temporary colors has become highly popular to add emphasis to the haircut; however, don't spend too much time in this area for it can over extend the service. A great barber never holds a client too long and he never rushes his client. The goal is to find that comfortable balance between the two states of time.

Now that your fade is complete use your mirrors to cross check your work. Make sure all lines are even and clean. Rotate a few times slowly from left to right to make sure your blending flows evenly and clean. Sanitize your client, release him/her with a handshake, and then sanitize your tools and station.

Conclusion

The goal of binary barbering is to give the reader a systemic approach to fading and blending. Using a combination of theoretical laws and mathematical principle to remember your work as you work. This process can and will cut fading time in half or more for the user who knows exactly every move they're going to make before they make it so thinking becomes obsolete!

Repetition of this system will allow one to work off memory, like a robot, for example. You can actually use this system on any type of fade they can name. Once mastered you will learn how to shorten the method only using certain steps to complete your fade.

The power of your knowledge as a barber increases the power in your abilities. Binary barbering is a fun and exciting way to learn fading! Work in the name and the brain of a master barber and serve well.

Remember the secret to this elite technique is in the mathematical system it employs. The secret mathematical code to Binary Blending is: (3, 5, 1, 4, 2).

Study and practice to perfection!!!!!!!!!!!!!!

P.E.A.C.E.

DEATH OF THE CELEBRITY BARBER

Memories of my youth are filled with vivid images of my father and I taking our voyages to the barbershop. The Men who imparted wisdom, knowledge, guidance, comfort, and compassion developed a place where the structure of who I am now, and the usual laughs while the buzzing of the clippers resonated thru the air.

I choose to believe that it was pure LOVE of an ability and pure LOVE of the clients that motivated these MEN to be the role models within the community I lived in...not only mine but yours, as well. A place where children would be able to hang out for the day while earning a few dollars but picking up JEWELS of life. A place where MEN would take a person in need, who was torn down by life, and build them back up. A place that would rejuvenate the spiritual as well as the physical. This is what I remember from my growth to a Man.

"Barbering" (yes, I made it up!), which is sad and pathetic! Where haircutters (NOT BARBERS), no longer put their patrons first and care about them but only see them as $$$ signs. Regarding our abilities as hustler's and not as Leaders or as Mentors. Bombarding our patrons with pervious smells of tobacco or marijuana, while claiming to be professional! They have lost the natural ability only to cover up flaws with a façade displayed by various forms of enhancing products.

Haircutters nowadays are more concerned with "likes" and "followers" than what WE were ORDAINED to do: MENTOR, LEAD, GUIDE, BUILD UP (and not to destroy), all while providing a SERVICE! Even owners have begun to "Bastardize" the profession by looking at their co-workers as $$$ and not as a FAMILY, where they allow sub-par cuts to walk out the shop without fixing them and educating the co-worker. Where they allow co-workers to treat the shop as drug dealers do the block, with the same mentality. Where owners no longer GIVE to the community but only desire to TAKE from those around...Industry Vultures.

I despise all of you who make us MEN in the industry look bad! Who only do it for the popularity, the $$$ and the fake image you display. You may have some of your clients fooled...but not US! Your time is limited because the MOVEMENT HAS BEGUN!

Words by Mr. Brian Henderson
Master Barber/ Master Barber Educator

"BARBER INTEGRITY"

"What is barber integrity?" should be the first question that comes to the mind of a conscious barber. To the mind of an unconscious barber, the question might be, "is there such a thing?"

In any event, conscious or unconscious "barber integrity" is a barber's ability to be truthful, honest, and stand on certain principles and morals. In short "upstanding in his/her word, ways, and actions.

I'll never forget my first day of Barber School. The first thing my instructor taught his 20 incarcerated students was, "this is an honorable profession, a fraternity, a brotherhood, and barbers don't TALK BAD about other barbers!"

These words of wisdom came from one of North Carolina's greatest barber educators in our states history. Now mind you this set the foundation for me to stand on as a professional barber. Those words little did I know would save a few lives some years later in my career as a professional barber.

How my other classmates took those words I will never know but in my mind, back in 2008 it said to me that barbers ride or die for one another...lol.

Mind you, I was a part of a prison program that allowed me to come home a license barber and have a functional career. I've always been a man of code and ethics first and employee second, so to me barbering was serious. This meant that I would have brothers and sisters everywhere in the world that I should be able to network with or call on if I needed help. It meant LOYALTY TO ONE ANOTHER!

I came into this business with my word and I will leave with my word yet there are a few in this world that I cannot pardon, for the transgressions of the wicked shall be destroyed. In my short-lived career, thus far, I've seen these words on both sides of the coin. I've seen the love and goodness it brings from alike barbers in this profession and I've seen the ugliness it brings out of barbers that only wish to blood suck off the people and their wealth and their own self built images.

Barber integrity is under attack! As we progress in the direction of an industry, "INTEGRITY" is becoming a thing off the past. In this body of work, I will address key points in this lesson for conscious barbers to hear and examine further. Unconscious barbers will only find ways to challenge and discredit the clear truth I will reveal at no gain of my own. The goal is only to make knowledge born of facts that effect our clients. For they are the victims in all of our self-made madness as barbers whom claim to be celebrities and the blood sucking companies that employ and exploit them for mass financial gain.

So, yes, I ask you... What is barber integrity?

Chapter One
Who or What is a Celebrity Barber?

When I first started doing research upon this subject I did as I've always done, I went to one of my elder barbers. In today's barber profession, one must stay in tune with those whom have paved the way for us. An elder barber or master barber is like a divine gatekeeper to the tree of knowledge that an understudy must earn rights to consume.

My elder immediately laughed and said, "I'm not sure when it started but I do know it is something we made up ourselves."

At that moment, I was hell bent on finding the origin of such a man-made beast, and why is this beast being placed on a pedestal.

Leaving no stone unturned I asked not one, not two, but I sought wisdom from all my teachers to date and the answer was basically the same, "it's something man-made!"

One elder even went as far as explaining to me that the popularity of this false title came about by way of Steve Harvey's barber and the illusion they gave the world with the infamous "Steve Harvey hairline".

Truly I found it odd that my elders one whom is a 5th generation barber held no respect for this false title. I found it odd that they all agreed that this false title was something made up by us (barbers) for whatever reason.

It gives me great honor to be in a position to reveal to my barber brothers and sisters that there is a deeper and more sinister plan in play here and unconscious barbers are doing the dirty work.

Who is the Celerity Barber? In all reality, a celerity barber is a barber that lacks proper knowledge of him or herself. A celerity barber is an industry slave that does not respect the history of this profession. A celerity barber is a bloodsucker of the poor that feeds on their own EGO and seeks to be praised and worshipped.

In short, a celerity barber is a man-made industrialized slave that lacks proper knowledge of self as a Barber.

These individuals develop over a course of time a huge vain EGO that eventually robs these types of barbers of their BARBER INTEGRITY.

These individuals have false images that they must uphold in order to stay in good standings with the people that set the guidelines for them to exist in.

These individuals are more concerned with their social public rather than their everyday clients. They seek to be worshipped and praised for whatever reason.

In all reality, if these self-absorbed individuals were truly in tune with their BARBER HISTORY they would already know that we as BARBERS have been the most important people in our communities since the beginning of our history dating back to the Glacier Age.

It's dangerous to the preserving of our history when barbers take it upon themselves to create such a title as "Celerity Barber" and then create such a vain life style and splinter cell of barbers that pose as the leading standard for ALL BARBERS.

Even worse we allow Companies to EMPLOY & SUPPORT these vain barbers and they control and make money off all other barbers even our clients with their so-called trade shows, staged barber battles, and so on. What does it say to a governing body (State Board) when barbers begin to do things on their own accord, and then try to make it law? Of course, they come and shut things down!

DEATH OF THE CELEBRITY BARBER...

Chapter Two
Corporate Barbering vs. Grassroots Barbering

Tried and tested beyond measure is how I describe my past year as a barber. Not to mention the heavy woes of my personal life dealing with a fresh separation and new born baby on the way after losing my first-born son. One would say many a negative things about me, yet my actions would trump their efforts every time. Even in light of all my worldly madness I still managed to develop multiple business facets, etc.: J.B.A., BY FADE GRIFFIN, NORTH CAROLINA BARBER AWARD SHOW & HONORS CEREMONY, B.R.F., just to name a few.

It may seem that I've gotten off topic, yet the above serves merit. On both sides of the coin in one year I managed to live five years. No ego...just culture.

I have been many places and seen many things. I've been as far up as Delaware, as low as Florida, and as wide west as Laredo, Texas. I've gathered information, shook hands, overcame transgressors, rode the wings of faith, and experienced near death.

It all started around June/July when I walked out without clear warning on my salary-paying job at Park West. At that time, no one around me could cee as far as I could.

I whispered what was to "BE" to a chosen few as the word of God in me took flesh one revelation after another, day after day. If I could touch the skyline my hands would no longer BE.

On this journey, I uncovered the hoax being promoted by an industry that only exist in theory. The more I traveled and learned the more I learned about life and our profession.

As I worked and served my community like a true grassroots barber, unbeknownst to me there was a group of people working against us all. Over the past five years corporate barbering has been on the rise with the help of social media and numerous companies popping up.

One might ask what is corporate barbering? Corporate barbering is where companies dish out haircuts on an assembly line with no personal relationship at all. Corporate barbering is also the companies we give power to like Andis, Whals, Oysters, etc. These are the people that we allow to say what a barber is supposed to look like, sound like, dress like, and BE like.

Grassroots barbering is simply practicing barbering in its natural form. Barbering is a culture and not an industry. The last time we allowed a culture to be industrialized we killed it (**HIP-HOP).** Celerity barbers or these companies' slaves have said to our industry, "we don't want your old ways anymore because they pay us more to be man-made."

In short, grassroots barbers are FREE and corporate barbers are **SLAVES TO A FALSE INDUSTRY.**

Just look at the condition of celebrities in other industries and now take a look around your own so-called industry. Every day, you can find a new barber somewhere immolating what they've seen another barber somewhere else do. Everyday a barber somewhere is using another barber's work as their own on their business card trying to lure clients to the barbershop for a lowball haircut. This is the work of your so-called industry and the celebrities you celebrate!

Chapter Three
Barbers are the New Emcees

Instead of saying, "mic check 1, 2, 1, 2," barbers say, "I'm building my brand so that one day I can be chosen."

Who are you wanting to be chosen by is the question! The answer is clear. These so-called brand-building barbers want to be chosen by the new record labels, which are the companies we allow to exploit our culture etc.: Andis, Wahls, Oysters. Isn't it bad enough these companies already get our continuous business from manufacturing and selling us tools?

At one time barbers wanted to be platform artists for these companies, which is cool. These companies use barbers to whoa crowds of our clients with their hair cutting skills and knowledge to ultimately sell them tools and products for our trade. These companies use the barber to do their dirty work. They exalt whom they wish. Brand them in their image (how they think you should look), and then pay these hand selected barbers a nice salary so they can serve as someone everybody in the industry wants to be and strive for. In theory, this is cool; but, in all reality, this is making a barber a slave and these companies are the slave masters.

Barbers in pursuit of this level of man-made barbering are the ones with the terrible attitudes. These are the barbers that have a Kayne-sized EGOs, but a peanut size barbercation. These are the barbers that infringe upon **BARBER INTEGRITY.**

I've encountered numerous barbers over the past year that are putting more emphasis on themselves than their clients. They focus more on who they think they are than who they really are and should be as a barber. A great deal of the problem starts with Barber School. In today's barber profession, even the ranks of our education department have become corrupted by the love of money and financial aid. Students come out of Barber School thinking that they are Master BARBERS. We have grown a crop of young ignorant barbers that only copy and paste to their lives what they see and hear on social media. The same barbers that they see and praise on these social sites don't even have half the barbercation that they have, yet they seek to praise these barbers and to be praised themselves.

Think about it, what better way to control a group of people that are free than to create an industry out of their culture and then give them standards to live by so that they will be accepted by those whom control and dictate the industry.

These new labels or so-called barber companies sign these slave-barbers to these 6 figure deals as if they were recording artists and younger barbers think that this is the ULITMATE LEVEL OF SUCCESS in our profession.

In reality, these slave-barbers are only looking for a bailout. They think that by becoming a celebrity barber or by cutting celebrities that they will become rich, wealthy, or well off.

As industry barbering is not only controlled or dictated by a chosen few but it also gives way for outside sources to leech off our profession. In example; Cedric The Entertainer and his BARBER BATTLE TV show was a horrible exploitation of our culture. Ice Cube as well is making millions off us with his movies and he doesn't have barber license the first. Even worse he doesn't even employ barbers to play roles in the movie, and they break numerous laws that we teach in safety and sanitation.

You know it's bad when I, an eight-year Master barber walks in a Wal-Mart and see a Gillette Razor display using our barber pole to market and sell their razors. In my book, this is open disrespect not only to me as a professional but also as a businessman. We have the nerve to wonder why the art of shaving in the barbershop has faded over the years. We have the nerve to wonder why we have fallen as a profession from the ranks of the medical profession. We have allowed outside influences to control and dictate who we are supposed to be and what and how we are supposed to do it.

Barbering will be like working at McDonalds in the near future if we continue to allow people to make up what they wish as they go in this profession. A sell-out doesn't care about who or what they sell-out as long as they are the one reaping the benefits. To these new emcees I say, "instead of selling your soul to a false industry, study more, learn more, serve the people of your chosen community, and sell your soul as a barber to the uplifting and advancing the science of our culture."

DO NOT COMMIT BARBER GENOCIDE BY EMPOWERING AN INDUSTRY THAT WILL INDUSTRILIZE OUR CULTURE AND ENSLAVE US BY THEIR STANDARDS.

Chapter Four
Barbers are Having an Identity Crisis

In 2017 barbers do not know who they are! There is a serious IDENITY CRISIS in our profession mainly because there is a lack of emphasis on correct barber history. In this day and time, the hardest thing to teach a new barber is that what they see on social media is not what we are really about. Students will post a cut straight out of Barber School knowing they need more work yet they post imperfections and all. Chasing some type of fame, from WHO! Who are you really trying to impress? What did you learn in BARBER SCHOOL?

As an instructor at Park West I studied and learned many things about our students. I successfully learned their habits, their fears, life challenges, and most importantly their true intent for being on this journey.

Even at the ground level of our profession our future barbers still fail to learn who they are! About the most they can say is that they were once a part of the medical profession, and that they are their own BOSS!

We had students that had barber names before they had a barber's license! One might say, "he's just hating," and they would be correct. I hate the fact that the PASSION for this profession gets pushed to the side for whatever reason one might have but we all know "MONEY" is their main motivation.

Money and false industry fame have become the FINISHLINE pursuit for a lot of new barbers because this is being PROMOTED as WHO WE ARE SUPPOSED TO BE AS BARBERS.

Suffering from this current identity crisis barbers are falling victim to their own madness. Take a look on any popular social media site and see the circus show barbers are putting on. We have so many trends going on at one time it's confusing to a said degree about WHO WE REALLY ARE! We have all type of videos making fun of our profession, and we laugh along. We have barbers using other barbers work for their own work just to lure clients into their chair. We have barbers painting clients with all types of color enhancements to cover their own imperfections instead of the clients. We have barbers posting videos claiming that they are educating their audience, and they themselves have not furthered their own education as a barber. Students would trust these videos before they would trust their instructors mainly because we were right there with them and not HIGH IN THE PUBLIC EYE!

In short we have taken bad barbershop practices and made a lifestyle out of it with joking videos for views and likes on social media for a false capital gain.

Who are you barbers? Why did you become barbers in the first place? Do you really know what it means to be a barber?

The fruit never fall too far from the tree! I'm truly blessed as a barber because of the people that educated me to be a barber! I honor the men and women that ushered me into this BROTHERHOOD/SISTERHOOD. They all gave me pieces of a puzzle of who and what we are to BE as BARBERS. However, to be educated and trained by MR. HARRIS was the crowning jewel of my development into the MASTER BARBER/ MASTER BARBER EDUCATOR I'm growing to be today and forward. IT'S MOST IMPORTANT THAT A BARBER HAS A VISION FOR WHOM THEY WANT TO BE AS A BARBER! My advice is to allow this vision to develop internally and then practice every second of the day to deliver it externally to serve the people of the world with tact and honor!

Chapter Five
Barber Chair vs. Platform

As I think back I remember a debate we had in one of my 5 o'clock theory sessions. One of my young students was debating with another student about becoming a PLATFORM BARBER for Andis, saying that this was the only way to be truly successful as a barber.

Back then I laughed at the argument because I didn't know what I know now about the illusion of an industry and the agents (celebrity barbers) they employ. This particular student felt the way he felt because he was only thinking about the money, failing to realize that barbers that work for themselves are FREE-BARBERS, while barbers that work for ANDIS, WHALS, etc. are EMPLOYEES!

Yes. Don't get me wrong. Making six figures or whatever they make is good money but what about your SOUL? What about your INTEGRITY as a barber? What about the BROTHERHOOD/SISTERHOOD? Is money the only thing that drives you to be a Barber?

NOBODY WANTS TO STAND BEHIND THE BARBER CHAIR ANYMORE! Everybody wants to come out of Barber School and be PACINO! NOBODY WANTS TO BE EVERY-DAY-WORKING-IN-THE-SHOP BARBERS ANYMORE! Everybody wants to be a brand and do his or her own made up thing...UNTIL THE STATE BOARD COMES AROUND!

LET THE STATE BOARD COME IN YOUR SHOPS AND SEE HOW MUCH THEY CARE ABOUT YOUR BEING A CELEBRITY IF YOU'RE NOT IN COMPLIANCE WITH STATE LAW!

Working as a barber for someone else will never trump the barber that works for him or herself. No matter what stage their company sets for them, the stage of the barbershop is unmatched. The barbershop has always been the corner stone of our profession since time can be remembered. Barbershops are just as important in the world as churches are!

Chapter Six
Celebrity or Sellout

As a Master Barber Educator, I have grown to learn the importance of UNITY amongst barbers! I was educated as a barber since Barber School that we as barbers must be our best friend, our brother/sister, and our family! I was taught not to judge nor talk BAD about another barber. However, this does not hold true to ALL BARBERS.

In all reality, there are some real UNPROFESSIONAL BARBERS that come in the name of our profession but not the BRAIN of this culture! There are many barbers that only seek Fame and Money, which is cool yet true BARBERS ascend and learn of a HIGHER PURPOSE. Knocking no one, yet until you have experienced these types of EGO DRIVEN / MONEY AND FAME DRIVEN individuals listen to the clear truth in these words.

My first real encounter with this CORPORATE SLAVE BARBER (CELEBRITY BARBER) false-mentality syndrome was during my first "Barber Battle" on December 7, 2014 in downtown Greensboro. This was an event held by a very close brother of mine named, Mr. Brown.

This event was to be a BARBER BATTLE hosted and judged by two Celebrity Barbers, Angel @#$% and Sipp the *&^%$#@.

Recalling this event, I remember how excited some of our students were over the fact that these barbers were coming to the event based off their social media presence. In my mind, I was more focused on the event and my first real BARBER BATTLE. I was so excited until the truth of the night started to unfold.

The event was held at a classy sports bar down town Greensboro called The Zone. The atmosphere was very festive. Angel @#$% and Sipp the *&^%$#@ had stations set up with their barber products to purchase, and they interacted with other professionals that were present.

Nearing the battle that I was to compete in, a Fasted Fade Battle. A student of mine at the time noticed something strange about the set, that I noticed it as well, yet didn't say anything. For the fastest fade battle the lighting was very poor! Honestly, we were almost in the dark. Manny The Barber had a light strapped to his head for crying out loud. Lol.

After seeing the set up I knew instantly that this wasn't going to be a fair fight. There were four barbers in the competition. Manny The Barber, Manny's Apprentice Barber, another lesser whose name I don't recall, and myself. At this point it was a no brainer!

My finish time initially was around my normal Gate City Barbershop time, roughly under 8 minutes. However, my students and other barbers yelled out to keep going because we had a full 15 minutes to cut. Right then I knew I had invested my money into a rigged event. In reality I'm always the team player.

I've helped many in this profession in my short eight-year career, yet appreciation is different than praise or false worship. RESPECT is an entirely different subject.

After the celebrity host announced the winner, which was Manny's Apprentice, everybody that had good sense knew that something wasn't right. I, being a conscious brother, immediately began to analyze the full picture.

A: The event turn-out was a bust as far as tickets sold. There were only about 40 people in attendance.

B: The Zone was not free so there was rent to be paid.

C: The event promoter had to pay both celebrity barbers a fee.

D: Prize money had to be paid for each event.

Even if none of the above reasoning points are not correct the fact still remains that out of three different barber battles all the winners were a part of the promoter's team.

NOTHING IS BY CONIENDENCE! The celebrity barbers put on a fantastic display of acting like they didn't know whom the winners were before the competitions begun. IS THIS NOT ROBBERY? The promoter and his team of winners took numerous pictures flaunting their rigged victories as planned, yet it was only to save them from losing money in the event.

What about all the other barbers that paid $50 or more to either compete or be involved in this event? In my mind, it felt no different than a rigged talent showcase for an independent music artist. Shady promoters robbing people of money and all they want to do is chase their dream of being a professional recording artist.

BARBERS ARE THE NEW RAPPERS AND THE COMPANIES WE EMPOWER (INDUSTRY) ARE THE RECORD LABELS!!!

Chapter Seven
Along Came a Celebrity Barber

"What about my image?" These words resonate in my mind like a bad taste in someone's mouth.

Imagine receiving the conception of an idea from the Almighty so powerful, that everyone you revealed it to only wanted to steal it or make it their own as if they were the creator.

The idea being stated was The North Carolina Barber Award Show & Honors Ceremony. This event was to be the first of its kind in our profession. It was to serve as a medium for which to bring unity and support amongst professionals in our profession here in North Carolina.

Recalling a dream I had one night back in 2014, I awoke and immediately began to scribe down what I brought out of my dream. When the writing was done the above idea had been given birth.

The Award Show was to show appreciation to those whom had worked hard and served all year long. The Honors Ceremony was to show respect to those who helped me become the barber I am today and our State Board was to be honored for their services as well.

For an entire year I kept this idea silent within myself until I felt like it was time to take flesh.

Finally, the date was set for November 1, 2015. The event was originally slated to be held at the Duke Event Center in Raleigh, which would've made for a grand event. However, at this time in my personal history I was in a double fight against life. I was currently in a terrible separation after three years of a depressing marriage and I had to deal with being apart from my newborn son.

Not to mention just five months before this original event I humbly walked away from a $40,000 annual salary with Park West. I also humbly relinquished my position at the number one barbershop in Greensboro, NC (Gate City Barber Shop) to one of my former student's, Mr. Thomas Stevens. He was to carry on the good name of our business establishment.

At this position, I was sure to produce at least another $20k part time. Hell, just five years ago I was making 40 cents a day, and I gave all of it up due to the above situations.

In light of it all I was still strong enough to survive with my clippers and God-given abilities to be a barber (Humble Server of Humanity).

The first attempt to stop the award show came when my soon to be ex-wife conspired in some sort with a former barber brother by the name of Phlashlight. This serpent of a brother in the garden of barber Eden sought to bring shame to me in some sort, by inviting me to work for him in his newly built by us barber shop in a corporate mall in Sanford, Florida, home of Trayvon Martin.

First of all, I guess the serpent and his Eve thought I was weak or desperate because I was willing to make the move. Honestly, I was trying hard not to go back to the penitentiary for LIFE.

They found it unbelievable that I would go so far away from my newborn son. This disbelief lead to this serpent violating numerous laws of nature that would result in swift justice in the court of the ALMIGHTY.

The first sign was when I held my very first Youth Event in Mt. Olive, NC at the Boys & Girls Club, thanks to the blessings of Ms. Cent Jones.

Even though this event brought together our community we grew up in, we raised close to $100 to build a youth barber program called J.B.A. (Junior Barber Association), which cut and ministered to the youth. Phlashlight tried to stop it by sending me on a wild goose chase to find a house to live in while in Florida.

Now on alert I was watching and listening twice as hard. Plans for the award show was on hold, yet I continued to plan in prayer while working around this serpent, while he was feeding Eve the entire time. Needless to say, the TRUTH revealed itself as conversation began to change and other serpent barbers were added to the equation, but once again I rose to the TOP with my clippers.

While in Florida, I fortified bonds with a network of barbers in Orlando that will last a lifetime, and Phlashlight was envious of this. I built a relationship with a Barber School that still wants to hire me even to this day to teach for them, because they like my natural approach as a Barber Educator.

This serpent was out to SHAME me, yet he taught me how to build a barbershop form the ground up...PRICELESS. He also taught me the dynamics behind corporate barbering (renting mall barbershops), and how to negotiate deals that will earn a sure profit for all parties...also, PRICELESS.

"The quietest fly on the wall will get smashed."

After leaving me stranded in Sanford, Florida, with only $15 to my name and all my four-year home worldly possessions I exiled myself for refuge from HELL OR JAIL to Laredo, Texas, where I was delivered and magnified.

When Mr. Harris called and asked me if I was sure about my move to Florida with Phlashlight, he said, "Be careful. It could be a snake in the grass!" Boy, was he RIGHT!

After leaving Florida, I migrated to Laredo, Texas to serve the people of that community with my barber brother, Clinton. This was the best move for me at the time for I knew and he knew what type of person I could be when people mistreat or disrespect me without just cause.

When I arrived in Laredo I had $7 to my name and began to cut out of a church fold-out chair. In four days' time, I had cut enough to purchase my barber chair and I was in business from there. With the help of my brother and the great people of Laredo, Texas, the Award Show was back on. Recharged and reloaded I began to piece the idea together from Texas so this meant that I would need help from people I could trust to handle the vision as I would in my absence. BIG MISTAKE!

I'll never forget the first wrong turn I took was connecting and hiring a certain lady barber to be the Host of the award show. This lady barber and I first connected through Instagram. I had reached out to her while at Park West to speak to the female barbers in my class, to motivate and inform them of some of the things women face in our profession. This phone call never took place because of conflicting schedules at the time, however, I hung on to her contacts in good faith.

About a year had passed (since that first connection) and some things had changed for us both, this said lady barber had went on to win the circus show Cedrick The Entertainer had on television, and for myself, I was a two-year barber instructor with the leading Barber School program in the world at the time with Park West.

Sometime in late August or early September of 2015, I reached back out this lady barber because of a post I saw she made on Instagram. After contacting her and sharing this great idea with her she was not only blown away but was more than ready to be a part of the event.

This lady barber began to open up doors in the social media world I never knew could be opened and I was impressed. In my heart I was like, "yes, I've finally found another barber that can hear the call and see the vision."

This lady barber was to be the host of the event alongside my great brother Rah-1 Artist for Team Collective out of Raleigh.

The relationship with the lady barber started out good and I honestly thought we were on the same page. I confided in her and told her face-to-face what we were up against in getting this event off the ground and into the flesh. I even told her about how my ex-wife and Phlashlight sought to cripple me so that the event wouldn't take place. She in turn assured me that this event was going to take flesh and that we would make it great. She even had people ready to invest and help me take the event to other states as I had already planned.

Turning a blind eye to the lady barber I had another problem brewing back home in North Carolina. Still not having my venue locked in and squared away financially I reached out to two well-known barbers in North Carolina and the industry. One was a very close brother of mine named Erick *&^%*& and the other was Frankie *&(^%$#. My goal was to bring these great brothers on board to help strengthen the unity among barbers in our state. However, these two brothers only led me on all the way up to the event as if they were going to join me and we all pull this event off as a collective.

The power of the all mighty dollar always overpowers the mind of greedy and disloyal people.

I guess Anthony and Erick felt like I wasn't the right association for them because Erick works for Andis and Anthony is with Bronner Brothers, and I'm independent. Man, this reminds me of the music majors vs. independent or mainstream vs. the underground.

Needless to say, these two brothers used our conversations about my event and put together their own event two months after mine. This knowledge fell upon me two days before my event! Is there not a clear pattern being formed here?

So here it was in my mind I'm thinking the event is set and is really going to happen the way I envisioned it. Here I was thinking I had assembled a very professional and elite group of leading barbers to help bring unity to our state and other states.

My wake up with the lady barber came from a strange phone call from her while she was in a hotel room in Denver at the time. The call was strange for two reasons. One because she had called me rather late in the night and she was crying or had been crying. She began to say how she was tired of this life and some of the people involved in this business. In my mind, I thought she might have just had a bad experience and assured her that she was going to be okay.

The second red flag came when she said her company was sending me an invoice to book her for my event.

The fee was for $750 plus travel expenses. When I received the invoice, it was something anyone could type up and print out for someone to sign. Come to find out the company she spoke about was that of her boyfriend, also a fellow barber brother and he was her manager. I paid her a $350 down payment and was prepared to book her flight for the event, because I knew it was a success on all levels not just financially.

Little did I know this lady barber had other intentions for being a part of this event. She had just received her instructor's license in which I thought she already had. The reason she opened up this door of other barbers would soon be revealed.

Two days before the event everything that could go wrong went wrong and I continued to fight for what I believed in. At this point it was a salvage mission with no venue and one day to find one.

Despite all the obstacles and back-biting individuals the event took flesh and was actually better than I could have imagined. Because the correct people showed up, we held a positive event and emitted a strong message to our state and barber community. For Christ's sake, I honored and gave out awards to our State Board for their services in our profession, as well.

Mrs. Carla Davis was blown away when I presented her with her Lifetime Achievement Award at the State Board office in Raleigh the next day.

Common sense would say that I wasn't able to fly the lady barber out from San Antonio to North Carolina for the event with one day remaining before the event and no venue. The next day after the event all hell was about to break loose!

Even though the event was a success there was still an important lesson about to be learned. The very next day the manager of the lady barber (which was her boyfriend) called me with disrespect in his tone. After a few minutes of arguing over the phone about the event the real truth finally came out. The lady barber out of rage grabbed the phone and said to me, "what about my image?!" This statement made me lose my cool!

I remember yelling back, "Do you think I reached out to you for your image.?" I found it very disrespectful that the lady thought I booked her for her self-made image or for the contacts she had amassed over the years in her career. Out of all the challenges surrounding this event the above statement was hard for me to accept. I simply reached out to this lady barber because of her professionalism and the work she was doing in the name of our profession. Honestly, had I known that she only joined to build her image or strengthen her status amongst this secret circle of barbers, I would've never reached out to her for this event.

Yet hindsight is 20 – 20, so now I see things more clear when dealing with barbers plagued by this mode of thinking. In all reality, I shared this experience with you only to educate, not to discredit or disrespect anyone. The problem is not in the individual but in the train of thought the individual employs: "The celebrity barber syndrome".

Barbers have always been the most important figure in their chosen community. Now with the rise of social media and companies we empower, barbers no longer look at themselves as celebrities in their chosen community. Nowadays, barbers are seeking fame on a different level, which creates a selfish mode of thinking because the real and only celebrities are our clients! With that being said, ALL BARBERS ARE CELEBRITY BARBERS.

Chapter Eight
Too Many Barbers, Not Enough Barbercation

At this point the first question that is probably on your mind is what is Barbercation? Barbercation is a term I've created that is the combination of the two most important words in our profession, barber and education. So, in short, Barbercation is a barber's level of education.

Take myself for example! I've been to Barber School a total of three years and I attended a Continuing Education class to become a barber instructor at Wake Tech Community College. The average student only goes to Barber School once and at max their time only reaches 18-months or slightly more. However, I've been to Barber School once as a student for one year and then I taught at Park West in Greensboro for two years. So, in total, I've been in Barber School for three years.

In this time, I've grown in barbercation on all levels of our profession. Things that I didn't learn as a student I mastered as an instructor. Why is this important? Mainly because my clients know that they are receiving an educated barber.

Clients ask me all the time why do I have two licenses and other barbers they see ma as only having one. I simply say it's because I chose to further my education as a barber. In fact, every year I assign myself different tasks to learn as a professional.

Whether if it's a new cut for a man or woman, or if it's just simply researching the profession as a whole to see where improvement is needed.

In my professional opinion continuing education for barbers is highly needed – not only in North Carolina, but abroad. Each year our sister profession (Cosmetology professionals) must have at least 40 hours of Continuing Education. Honestly, I think that barbers should be held by the same standard. The biggest mistake a student makes coming out of Barber School is forfeiting what they were taught while in school for what they see going on around them in and outside the shop.

My instructor warned us every day, "don't pick up on old shop habits after Barber School!" It's crazy how freshly graduated barber students want to chase a dream, as they refer to it, of being a celebrity barber but can't follow a simple rule they were taught in Barber School called not "breaking the pole".

It's crazy how barbers want to be a highly celebrated person (celebrity) but fail to clean their clippers between every client. Honestly barbers, what is most important? You or the client?

In the North Carolina rules and laws governing its barbers, it states that the number one concern of our barber board is the safety of the public.

In closing, barbers look around and ask yourselves, "Why are we as barbers being commercialized at such a rapid and alarming rate?" I'd like for all barbers to look in the mirror and say, "My client is the real celebrity and my oath is to serve him/her to the highest of my ability, so that they in turn will celebrate me!"

Also remember according to our history, Meryma'at is the only barber-to date-to have a statue made in his image for the service and teachings he practiced in the (Kemetic) Egyptian community.

Barbers are multi-faceted individuals that excel in different aspects of business and barber theology. Barbers will always be celebrated people without having to celebrate themselves. This profession is not for self-idol worship, which erodes the fibers of integrity and unity in or profession. If we celebrate our clients, they will always celebrate us as professionals and not as celebrated individuals.

When Jay-Z released D.O.A. (Death Of Auto-tune) in 2009 it wasn't to diss people per se, yet it was to call attention to his industry. Too many people were doing the same thing and trying to look and sound the same way. The need for creativity was at an all-time high and Jay-Z felt the need to express the importance of staying original in art form and craft.

Barbers, it is time to take action and demand control of our profession! The jokes are over and we've laughed at ourselves long enough. We have sold ourselves out for the wrong dollar and it's time to rebirth our history for future barbers to uphold and preserve.

P.E.A.C.E.

My Barber Prayer

He gave me power in my hands so that I may reach people. He gave me power in my mind so that I may teach people. He gave me compassion in my heart so that I may serve people. To the highest of my God-given abilities, and to H.I.M., I give all the Glory.

AMEN

ABOUT THE AUTHOR

Kendrick D. Henderson is a nine-year NC Master Barber/Master Barber Educator who has practiced barbering in the states of Virginia, Florida, Texas and Georgia (to-date).

Fueled with a sincere passion for the art and education of all barbers and barber enthusiasts worldwide, Kendrick Henderson has assisted the careers of many student barbers as well as established barbers in this profession.

Besides being an aspiring Barber Author, Kendrick Henderson has created a Barber Youth Program, his own Barber Corporation, and has also participated in numerous Barbering events serving the homeless nationwide. In short, his aim is to heal every man, woman, and child by employing the science of his beloved culture.

ORDER MORE BOOKS

Mail along with payment to: **P.O. Box 1483 Smyrna, GA 30081**

Name
_____

Address
_____

City
_____

State _____ Zip _____

Book		Qty	Total
	How To Fade Like Griffin by Kendrick Henderson *Genre: Educational* *Cost: $25.00/each**		$_____
	The Cartel's Daughter Unedited: Raw and Uncut! by Carmine *Genre: Crime/Thriller/Urban* *Cost: $14.99/each**		$_____
	Bullet Proof by Bodie Quinette *Genre: Self-Help/Motivational* *Cost: $15.95/each**		$_____
	The Pig Who Became President By Alana Johnson *Genre: Children's* *Cost: $12.95/each**		$_____
	Set Free by Truth By Amari Johnson *Genre: Children's* *Cost: $12.95/each**		$_____

*SHIPPING & HANDLING: *1-3 Books: $5.00* *4-9 Books: $9.00* *$3.95 each addt'l book*	$_____
TOTAL ENCLOSED	$_____

Acceptable Forms of Payment: *Money orders or U.S. bank issued checks made payable to* **The Solid Foundation Group***. Please do not send cash.*

Visit our website to learn more about our authors
and their books |or| to order online.
www.TheSolidFoundationGroup.com

CPSIA information can be obtained
at www.ICGtesting.com
Printed in the USA
BVHW04s1725050718
520789BV00032B/961/P